CHAPPELL

LONDON

CHAPPELL
LONDON

THE ANNIVERSARY WALTZ	4
ANYTHING GOES	10
AROUND THE WORLD	14
BEWITCHED	16
THE BLUE ROOM	20
BODY AND SOUL	24
DANCING IN THE DARK	28
DEAR LITTLE CAFE	32
EMBRACEABLE YOU	36
EV'RY TIME WE SAY GOODBYE	40
HELLO DOLLY	7
HOW ARE THINGS IN GLOCCA MORRA?	60
IF EVER I WOULD LEAVE YOU	44
IF LOVE WERE ALL	48
I'LL SEE YOU AGAIN	52
I'VE GOT YOU UNDER MY SKIN	56
JUST LOVING YOU	68
KEEP THE HOME FIRES BURNING	71
LOVE STORY (WHERE DO I BEGIN)	76
LOVE WALKED IN	78
THE MAN I LOVE	82
MOON RIVER	86
THE MORE I SEE YOU	96
MY FUNNY VALENTINE	88
MY HEART STOOD STILL	92
NEAR YOU	99
ON THE STREET WHERE YOU LIVE	102
ROSES OF PICARDY	108
SOMEONE TO WATCH OVER ME	112
STAY AS SWEET AS YOU ARE	116
TEA FOR TWO	118
TENDERLY	122
THERE'S A SMALL HOTEL	124
TIME AFTER TIME	128
TRY TO REMEMBER	131
WE'LL GATHER LILACS	134
WHEN I FALL IN LOVE	142
WHEN YOU WISH UPON A STAR	138
YOU'LL NEVER KNOW	140

Edited by Peter Foss and Stephen Clark

© 1992 Chappell Music Ltd

International Music Publications,
Southend Road, Woodford Green,
Essex, England.

1-2-51139

THE ANNIVERSARY WALTZ

Words and Music by AL DUBIN & DAVE FRANKLIN

SEE PAGE 6 FOR
INTRODUCTION AND VERSE

REFRAIN
Valse moderato (*tenderly*)

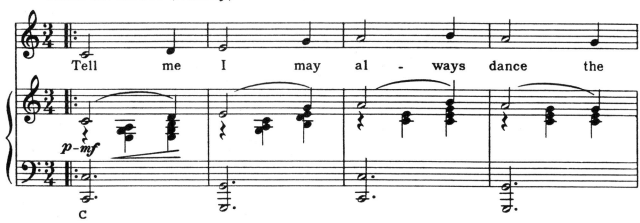

Tell me I may al - ways dance the

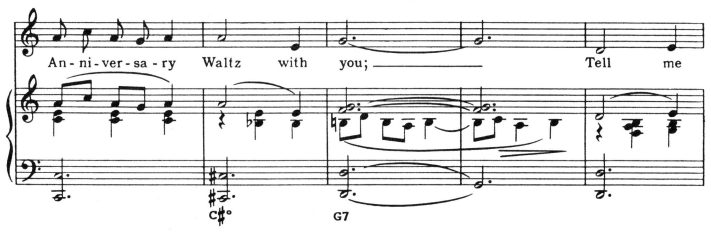

An - ni - ver - sa - ry Waltz with you; _____ Tell me

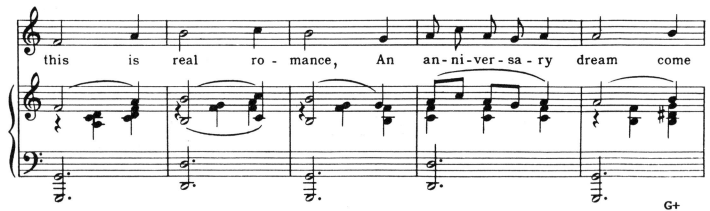

this is real ro - mance, An an - ni - ver - sa - ry dream come

5

true. _____ Let this be the an - them to our fu - ture

C   C#°   G7   C7   F

years, To mil - lions of smiles and a few lit - tle tears.

A+   D7   G7+

May I al - ways list - en to the An - ni - ver - sa - ry

C   A7   D7

Waltz with you. _____   you. _____

G7   C   Dm   G   C

Fine

INTRODUCTION AND VERSE

HELLO DOLLY!

Words and Music by JERRY HERMAN

mor - row will be bright - er than the good old days!

rit.

Refrain - Medium Strut tempo

HEL - LO, DOL - LY, well, HEL - LO, DOL - LY, It's so nice to have you

u tempo

mp - mf

back where you be-long. You're look-ing swell, Dol-ly, we can tell,

Dol-ly, You're still glow-in', you're still crow-in', you're still go - in' strong. We feel the room

ANYTHING GOES

Words and Music by COLE PORTER

Moderato

VERSE

Times have changed And we've of-ten re - wound the clock

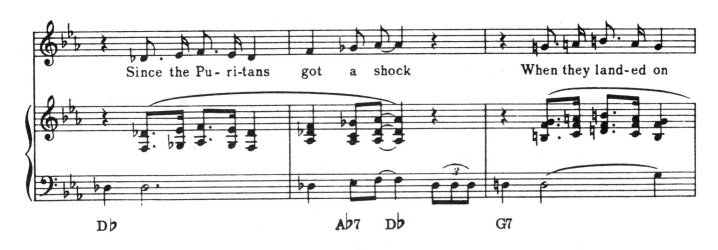

Since the Pu - ri-tans got a shock When they land-ed on

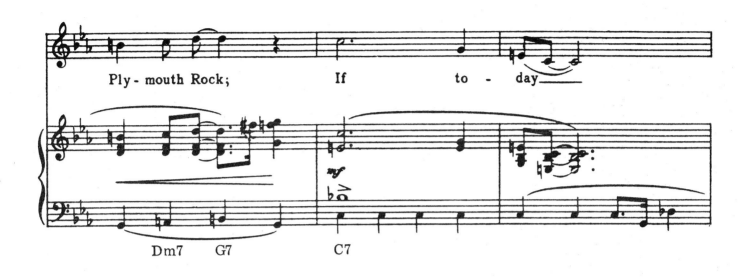

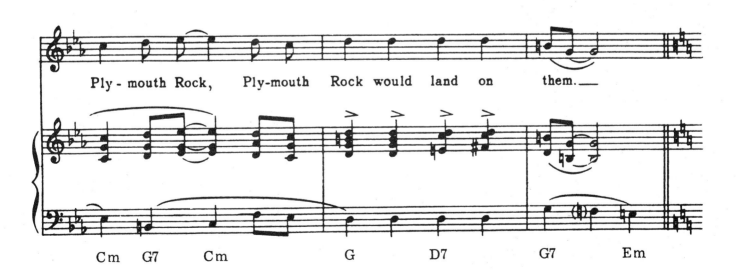

12

AROUND THE WORLD

Words by HAROLD ADAMSON
Music by VICTOR YOUNG

15

BEWITCHED

Words by LORENZ HART
Music by RICHARD RODGERS

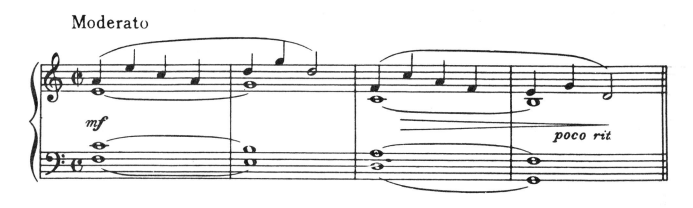

Love's the same old sad sen-sa-tion, La-te-ly I've not slept a wink,

Dm7   G7   C   Dm7 G7   C   A7

Since this half-pint im-i-ta-tion, Put me on the blink.

Dm7   G7   C   Dm7   G7

REFRAIN *(slowly)*

I'm wild a-gain, Be-guiled a-gain, A sim-per-ing, whim-per-ing

p-mf a tempo

C   G7   C   C+

child a-gain, Be-witched, both-ered and be-wild-ered am

F   G#dim C   D7   G7   A7

THE BLUE ROOM

Words by LORENZ HART
Music by RICHARD RODGERS

REFRAIN

Slowly, *with expression.*

We'll have a blue room, A new room, For two room, Where

ev - 'ry day's a hol - i - day Be - cause you're mar - ried to me.

Not like a ball-room, A small room, A hall room, Where

{I/you} can smoke {my/your} pipe a-way, With {your/my} wee head up-on {my/your} knee.

23

BODY AND SOUL

Words by ROBERT SOUR, EDWARD HEYMAN & FRANK EYTON
Music by JOHN GREEN

DANCING IN THE DARK

Words by HOWARD DIETZ
Music by ARTHUR SCHWARTZ

DEAR LITTLE CAFE

Words and Music by NOEL COWARD

REFRAIN

EMBRACEABLE YOU

Words by IRA GERSHWIN
Music by GEORGE GERSHWIN

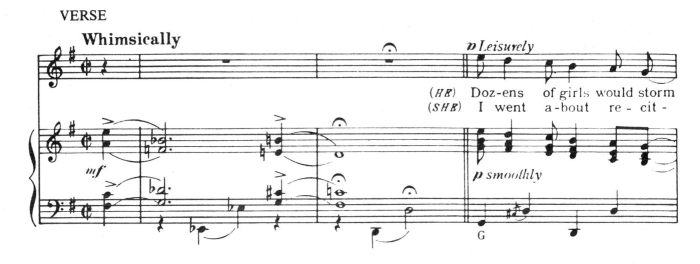

REFRAIN (*Rhythmically*)

EV'RY TIME WE SAY GOODBYE

Words and Music by COLE PORTER

43

IF EVER I WOULD LEAVE YOU

Words by ALAN JAY LERNER
Music by FREDERICK LOEWE

IF LOVE WERE ALL

Words and Music by NOEL COWARD

50

I'LL SEE YOU AGAIN

Words and Music by NOEL COWARD

55

I'VE GOT YOU UNDER MY SKIN

Words and Music by COLE PORTER

HOW ARE THINGS IN GLOCCA MORRA?

Words by E Y HARBURG
Music by BURTON LANE

62

HOW HIGH THE MOON

Words by NANCY HAMILTON
Music by MORGAN LEWIS

breeze just made it bree - zy, And then I

fell in love, And things that once were clear

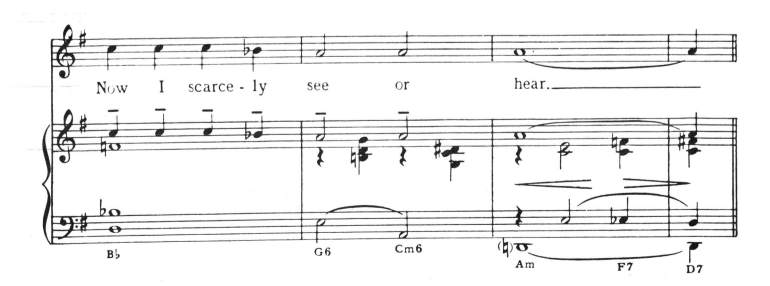

Now I scarce - ly see or hear.

66

REFRAIN (Slowly, with expression)

Some-where there's mu - sic,_____ How faint the tune!_____

_ Some-where there's hea - ven,_____ How high the moon!_____ There is no

moon a - bove When love is far_ a -way, too,_____ Till it comes

true_____ That you love me as I love you. Some-where there's

JUST LOVING YOU

Words and Music by TOM SPRINGFIELD

Steady tempo (with feeling)

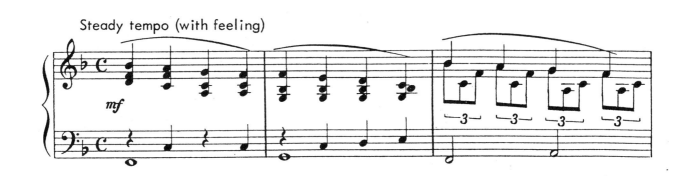

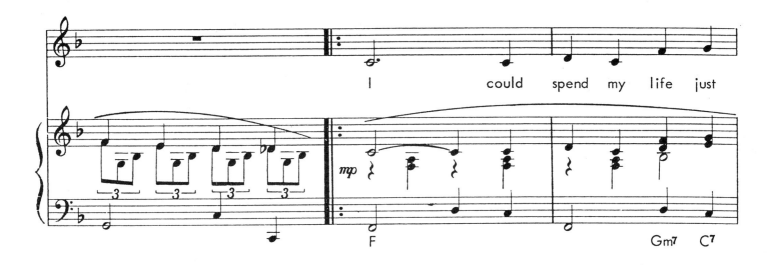

I could spend my life just

lov - ing you, _____ If you could learn to fall in love with

KEEP THE HOME FIRES BURNING

Words by LENA GUILBERT FORD
Music by IVOR NOVELLO

74

Refrain.

LOVE STORY (WHERE DO I BEGIN)

Words by CARL SIGMAN
Music by FRANCIS LAI

LOVE WALKED IN

Words by IRA GERSHWIN
Music by GEORGE GERSHWIN

THE MAN I LOVE

82

Words by IRA GERSHWIN
Music by GEORGE GERSHWIN

84

MOON RIVER

Words by JOHNNY MERCER
Music by HENRY MANCINI

MY FUNNY VALENTINE

Words by LORENZ HART
Music by RICHARD RODGERS

90

MY HEART STOOD STILL

Words by LORENZ HART
Music by RICHARD RODGERS

VERSE

1. I laughed at sweet.. hearts_____ I met at
2. Through all my school - days_____ I ha - ted

schools;_____ All in - dis - creet hearts
boys._____ Those A - pril Fool days

94

Slow but liltingly (molto tranquillo)

REFRAIN

THE MORE I SEE YOU

Words by MACK GORDON
Music by HARRY WARREN

**SEE PAGE 98 FOR
INTRODUCTION AND VERSE**

REFRAIN

The more I see you,___ The more I want you.___ Somehow this

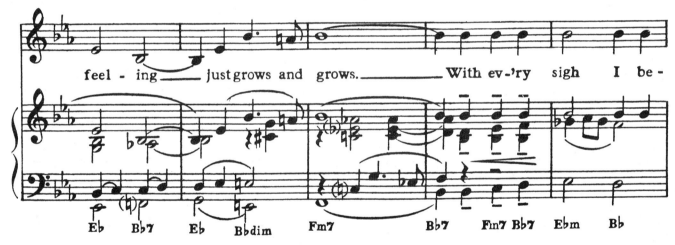

feel - ing___ just grows and grows.___ With ev-'ry sigh I be-

-come more mad a - bout you,___ more lost with-out you___ And so it

98

INTRODUCTON AND VERSE

Andante

VERSE

Each time I look at you is like the first time, __ Each time you're

Eb   F9   Bb7aug   Eb   Bbdim

near me, __ the thrill is new. __ And there is nothing that I would-n't

Fm7   Bb7   Eb   Bb7   Eb   F9   Cdim

do for, the rare de-light of __ the sight of you. For; __

G   Ddim   Am7   D7   G7 Bbdim F7   F7b5 Bb7

rit.

NEAR YOU

Words by KERMIT GOELL
Music by FRANCIS CRAIG

Moderato

mf

VERSE

mp

Some folks like the coun-try, fish-ing in a stream, Oth-ers like the

F   F#dim   C7   Gmi7   C7   Bb Cdim C7   Gmi7

moun-tains, that's where they can dream. Some folks like the ci-ty,

C9   Ami C7   Bb   F   Gmi7 C7   F   Ddim

love to see a show, I'm a lit-tle diff-'rent, don't care where I go.

C   G7 Cdim C6   A7   Dmi   FmiDmi7 G7   Gmi7   C7

REFRAIN *(rhythmically)*

ON THE STREET WHERE YOU LIVE

Words by ALAN JAY LERNER
Music by FREDERICK LOEWE

Words by ALAN JAY LERNER

ROSES OF PICARDY

Words by FRED E WEATHERLY
Music by HAYDN WOOD

SOMEONE TO WATCH OVER ME

Words by IRA GERSHWIN
Music by GEORGE GERSHWIN

STAY AS SWEET AS YOU ARE

Words and Music by MACK GORDON and HARRY REVEL

REFRAIN

TEA FOR TWO

Words by IRVING CAESAR
Music by VINCENT YOUMANS

known.   Far from the cry of the ci-ty,_____ where flow-ers
do.   SHE. All   of your schemes I'm ad-mir-ing,_____ they're worth de-

F   Ab7   Db   Eb7   Cm   Fm Db

pret-ty_____ car-ess the streams,   Co-sy to hide in,   to
-sir-ing;_____ but can't you see,   I'd like to wait, dear,   for

Dbm   Ab   Bb7   Ab   Eb

live side by side in,   don't let it a-bide in   my dreams.
some fu-ture date, dear.   It won't be too late, dear,   for me.

Ab   Eb7   Ab   Eb7   Ab Eb7 E7 F7

REFRAIN

Pic-ture you up-on my knee, just tea for two and two for tea; Just

p – mf

Bbm7   Eb7   Bbm7   Eb7   Abmaj7   Ab   Abmaj7   Ab

TENDERLY

Valse moderato

Words by JACK LAWRENCE
Music by WALTER GROSS

THERE'S A SMALL HOTEL

Words by LORENZ HART
Music by RICHARD RODGERS

TIME AFTER TIME

Words by SAMMY CAHN
Music by JULE STYNE

SEE PAGE 130 FOR
INTRODUCTION AND VERSE

REFRAIN

Time af - ter time I tell my - self that I'm So

luck-y to be lov - ing you, _____ So luck - y to

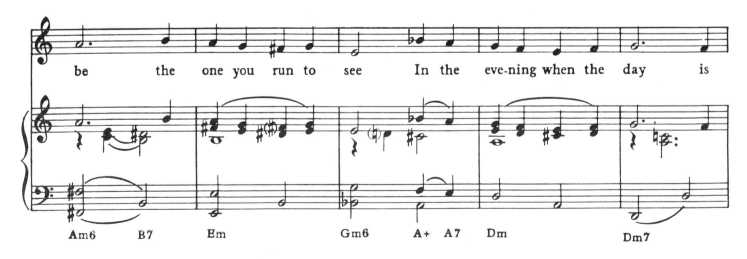

be the one you run to see In the eve-ning when the day is

130

INTRODUCTON AND VERSE

Moderato

mf

VERSE

ten.

What good are words I say to you?_____ They can't con-vey to you_____

mp

F   G   G9   C   E♭dim   Dm7

ten.

_____what's in my heart._____ If you could hear_____ in-

mf

G7   G9 B dim   C   Am   Am7   D7 Fdim

ten.

-stead_____ The things I've left_____ un - said!_____

rit.

C   G7   C   Am Am7   D7 Fdim   C   E♭7   Dm7 D♭9-5

TRY TO REMEMBER

Words by TOM JONES
Music by HARVEY SCHMIDT

1. Try to re - mem - ber the kind of Sep - tem - ber when
2. Try to re - mem - ber when life was so ten - der that
3. Deep in De - cem - ber it's nice to re - mem - ber al -

life was slow and oh, so mel - low.
no one wept ex - cept the wil - low.
tho' you know the snow will fol - low.

132

WE'LL GATHER LILACS

Word and Music by IVOR NOVELLO

136

REFRAIN

We'll gath - er li - lacs in the spring a - gain

And walk to - geth - er down an Eng - lish lane

Un - til our hearts have learned to sing a - gain

When you come home once more.

WHEN YOU WISH UPON A STAR

Words by NED WASHINGTON
Music by LEIGH HARLINE

YOU'LL NEVER KNOW

Words by MACK GORDON
Music by HARRY WARREN

WHEN I FALL IN LOVE

Words by EDWARD HEYMAN
Music by VICTOR YOUNG

SEE PAGE 144 FOR
INTRODUCTION AND VERSE

REFRAIN

When I fall in love it will be for - ev-er, Or I'll nev-er fall in

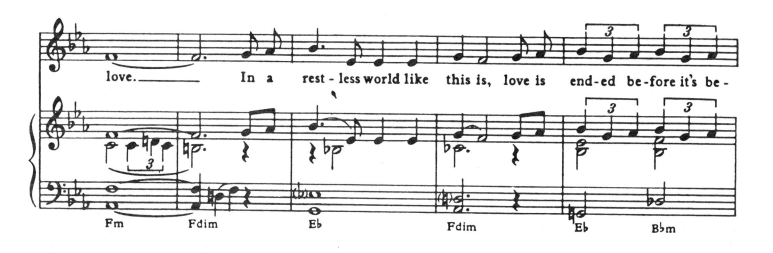

love._____ In a rest - less world like this is, love is end-ed be-fore it's be-

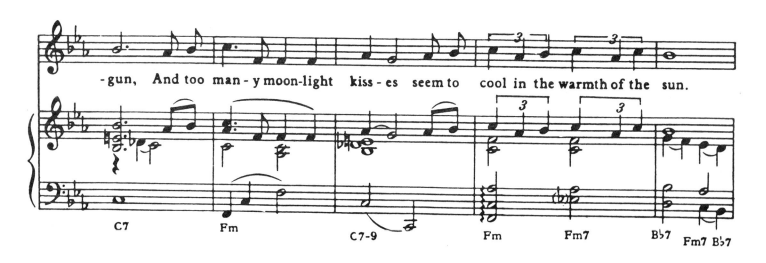

-gun, And too man-y moon-light kiss - es seem to cool in the warmth of the sun.

INTRODUCTION AND VERSE